Scott, Foresman Reading

Going Up

Program Authors

Ira E. Aaron
Dauris Jackson
Carole Riggs
Richard G. Smith
Robert J. Tierney

Book Authors

Dauris Jackson
Carole Riggs

Instructional Consultants

John Manning
Dolores Perez

Scott, Foresman and Company
Editorial Offices: Glenview, Illinois

Regional Offices: Palo Alto, California
Tucker, Georgia • Glenview, Illinois
Oakland, New Jersey • Dallas, Texas

CONTENTS

ISBN 0-673-14805-X
Copyright © 1983, 1981,
Scott, Foresman and Company, Glenview, Illinois.
All Rights Reserved.
Printed in the United States of America.

45678910-KPK-90898887868584

STORIES BY:

Judith Rosenbaum
Wendy Ableman
Andrew Weil
Duncan Searl

ACKNOWLEDGMENTS

"At the Zoo" from WHISPERS AND OTHER POEMS by Myra Cohn Livingston. Copyright © 1958 by Myra Cohn Livingston. Reprinted by permission of McIntosh and Otis, Inc.

"Clay" from THE MOON AND A STAR, © 1965 by Myra Cohn Livingston. Reprinted by permission of Harcourt Brace Jovanovich, Inc.

ILLUSTRATIONS

Cover: Norman Green
Kathy Allert: pages 29-32, 43-47; Lisa Bonforte: 24-27; James Dyekman: 53-57, 64-69; Will Harmuth: 70-75; Tien Ho: 33-37; Maggie MacGowan: 14-18, 38-41; Anthony Rao: 42, 48-52, 76-79; Christopher Santoro: 4-8; Stan Skardinski: 58-63; Pat Stewart: 19-23; George Suyeoka: 28; Jerry Zimmerman: 9-13.

Studio: *Kaeser and Wilson Design, Ltd.*

Find the Ball

A ball is under a box.

The cats look under the green box.

The dogs look under the blue box.

The bird and the mouse look under
the red box.

They all look for the ball.

They want to play with it.

4

The cats find the ball under
the green box.
They play with the ball.
Look at it go!
The dogs, the bird, and the
mouse play the game.
They all play with the ball.

Now the ball is going under the house.

The cats run to get the ball.

Are they going to get it?

Can the cats get under the house?

6

The cats want the ball.

They can't get it.

They want the dogs to get it.

The dogs can't get under the house.

The cats want the bird to get
the ball.

The bird can't get under the house.

Look at the mouse!
Can it get under the house?
The mouse is going under the house!
It is going to get the ball.
Now look what the mouse has.

The Ball Game

I want to play.
I want to play in a ball game.
I have bats and balls.
You and I can have a ball game.

 It is cold.
I can't play with you.
I can't play ball in the cold.
I want to go in the house.

 You and I can't play ball in the house.
I want to play ball.

10

 Look!

Look at all the socks you have.

With socks it is not cold.

With socks I can play in a ball game.

 Cat, you can have the red socks.
And you can have the yellow socks.
I can have the blue socks and the
green socks.

12

Now it is not cold.
It is not cold with socks on.
Now I want to play ball.

 I have all the bats.
I can bat this ball and this
ball and this ball.

 What a game this is!

All the Shops

 Look at all the shops!

 Come with me.
You and I can look in the shops.
I want to look at what the shops have.

What shop is this?
It looks like a good shop.

 Come in with me and look.

 Look at all the tables in this shop.
Tables are good to play under.
They are good to play house under.

This looks like a good shop.
Look at all the jars!
I can find red jars and blue jars.
And look at this giant yellow jar.
I can get in it.
I want a giant jar like this.

16

Come with me to this shop.

What a shop this is!

You can't get under this table.

And I can't get in this house.

This is a good shop to play in.

I like the jar shop.
It is the shop for me.
I like the giant jars in it.

And I like this shop.
In this shop I look like a giant.

18

Good for Animals

Look at this zoo.

It is not a good zoo at all.

It is not good for the animals.

It is not good to go to.

Can we help make this a good zoo?

 Look at all we have for the zoo.
What can we make to help the animals?

 We can make this wall blue and green.
We can make a new house for the animals.
We can make the animal yard look new.
We can all help.

20

Help me with this wall.
Help me make the wall look like new.
What can we make on it?

 I can help you make animals on the
wall.
The animals in the yard can look at
the animals on the wall.

Now we can make the animal yard look new.

We can make a new house for the animals.

We can make it in the yard.

The yard is going to look good.

The animals are going to like it.

22

Look! Now we have a good zoo.
The animals have a zoo they like.
They can run and play in the yard.
They can look at the animals on
the wall.
They can go in the new house.
We all like going to the zoo now.

Find the Animals

What animal can you find?

Look at the yard.

Look at the red box in the yard.

What is in it?

What animal is this?

This is the animal in the box.

24

Now look in the house.

Can you find the animal?

What animal can you find?

Is the animal green?

Is the animal yellow?

What animal is it?

This is the animal.

Look at this wall.

Find the animal.

Is the animal red?

Is the animal green?

Is the animal blue?

Can you find it?

This is the animal to look for.

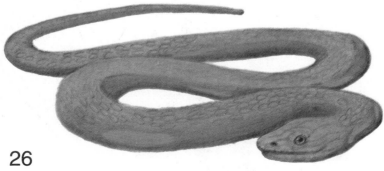

26

Look at this animal.

Can you find the animal like it?
Look under all the tables.
What table is the animal under?

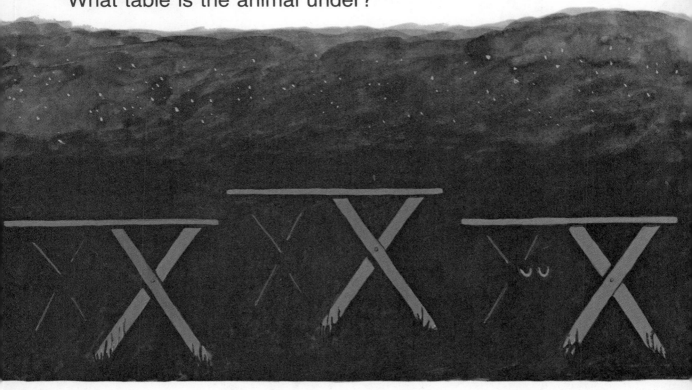

At the Zoo

by Myra Cohn Livingston

I've been to the zoo
    where the thing that you do
    is watching the things
    that the animals do

and watching
    the animals
    all watching

    you!

What Is Gilbert?

 I can't find Gilbert.
Can you help me find Gilbert?

 I can help you look for Gilbert.
We can look in the house and in
the yard.
We can find Gilbert.

 What is Gilbert?

 Gilbert and I like to play in the yard.
Gilbert can jump over this box.
Is Gilbert under the box now?
Quick, look in it!

 Gilbert is not under the box.

What can jump over a box?
What can get under a box?
What is Gilbert?

Gilbert and I like this wall.
Gilbert can jump on the vine and
run all over it.
Is Gilbert on the vine?
Gilbert is not on the vine.

What can jump and run on a vine?
What is Gilbert?

What animal can play like this?

What can go under a box?

What can jump over a box?

What can run all over a vine on a wall?

What is Gilbert?

32

What Can We Play?

 What can we play?

 I want to go out.
Can we play in your yard?
I want to run and jump in your yard.

We can't go out in the yard.
We can play house.
I want to play house.

But we play house all the time.
This time I want to play with
your ships.
Your ships are good to play with.

 But I want to play with a ship
I can get in.
We can't get in my ships.
Girls and boys can't get in a ship
like this.

34

I can make a ship for you to get in.
I can make it out of this chair.
Look! This is your ship.
And this is my ship.

 My ship is a big ship.
Look at it!
Look at what I can put on it.
Your ship is not big like my ship.

 My ship is not big.
But look!
I can get under my ship.
You can't get under your ship.

36

This is good.

I like to play on a ship like this.

It is good to run and jump in your yard.

But I like what we play in your house.

 Chairs make good ships.

They make ships we can play on.

Jars, Jars, Jars

Look at all the jars I have.
I have red jars and yellow jars.
Jars are on my table.
Jars are all over my chairs.
But what are jars good for?
What can I make with all my jars?

38

I can't make a house out of jars.

Jars can't make a good house.

A box makes a good house.

I can make a good house out of a box.

But jars?

Jars can't make good houses.

Can I make a table?
Can I make chairs?
I can't.
Jars can't make good tables.
Jars can't make good chairs.

40

But look at this!
Look what I can make!
I can make animals with my jars.
Jars can make good animals.
Look at all the animals I can make!
I can make all the animals for a zoo.

Clay

by Myra Cohn Livingston

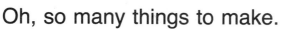

Oh, so many things to make.
A dog and a basket, a cat and a snake:
    I'm rolling,
    I'm pushing,
    I'm squeezing,
    I'm squishing,
    I'm poking,
    I'm pinching,
    I'm twisting,
    I'm wishing
    a piece of clay into a ring,
        a face,
        a flower—

        everything!

42

Sandy and Mandy

My name is Sandy Ramos.

My name is Mandy Ramos.
We look the same.
We have the same name.
It is Ramos.

 Mandy and I can jump over the
yellow box.
But I can jump over the red box.
Mandy can't.

44

Sandy and I like to ride.
Sandy can ride under the table.
I can't.
But I can ride with all my animals.

Mandy and I like to hide in the yard.
Can you find Mandy and me?

46

Mandy can make ships like this.

I can't.

I can jump like this.

Mandy can't.

Mandy and I look the same.

But we are not the same at all.

Finding Dan

 What is it, Willy?

 I wanted to play with Carmen.
Carmen likes to play with me.
But I have a cold.
I can't go out of the house.

48

 But you can have a good time.
I can play with you.
We can play in your house.
I can hide in your house.
And you can look for me.

 We can?
Good! Can you hide now?

 This box is good to hide behind.
I am not going to hide behind it.
But I am going to make Willy look
for me behind it.
This is what Willy is going to find.

Now I am going to hide behind this
chair.
The light is out.
Willy can't find me with the
light out.

The light is out.
But I can find you, Dan.
You are behind the box.

Dan? This is not Dan.
Dan is not behind this box.
What is Dan behind?

 What is behind the chair?
Dan, this time it _is_ you.
Come out, come out.

Willy, you are good at finding.
Now you can hide.
And I have to find you.

Giant Ben

Grandma and I like to play with Ben.

Ben is a giant.

Ben has a house behind my yard.

A shop is behind the house.

Ben makes ships in the shop.

Grandma and I like the ships Ben makes.

Look at this ship.

It is a giant ship.

It has giant tables and chairs in it.

It has giant lights on it.

It is a ship for a giant to ride in.

54

Ben has a ship for me.
It is for me and Grandma.
It is not a giant ship.
Ben can't ride in it.
But Grandma and I can.
We can ride all over in it.

Look at me in my ship.
Look at Grandma.
It is time for a ride.
Ben is going to help.
We ride behind Ben.
Ben makes the ship go.

56

Look! It is not light out now.
We can have a quick ride to the house.
Ben has the ship.
Ben has Grandma and me.
We ride on Ben to the house.
I like going on a giant ride.

Out They Come

Out comes the dog!

Out comes the clown behind the dog.

Out come Carla and Giant Jake.

They are going to make the boys and
girls laugh.

Giant Jake gets on the box.
Can the box hold Giant Jake?
Look at Jake on the box.
The box can hold Jake.
The boys and girls laugh at
Jake on the box.

The clown laughs and runs to Jake.
The clown puts a chair on Jake.
Carla and the clown help put the dog on
the chair.
What are they going to put on the dog?

Now Carla helps the dog jump down.

The clown holds on to the chair.

Now the dog wants to get on the swing.

Can a dog get on a swing?

This dog can.

Now Carla is going to ride Jake.
The clown helps Carla get on.
Carla likes to ride Jake.
Carla can look out at all the
boys and girls.
Look at Carla ride Jake.

It is time for Carla to get down.

The clown comes to help Carla.

But Carla slides down like this.

What a ride!

What a good time they all have.

The boys and girls laugh and laugh.

The New Shop

Kate and Sam see a new shop.
The new shop has books in it.
Kate and Sam want to go in.
Kate wants to pick out a book on ships.
And Sam wants to look at all the books.
Sam likes to read.

Kate and Sam go in.

They see books all over the shop.

Books are on tables and behind chairs.

Books are on top of books.

Look at all the books!
But they are not at all like the books
at my house.
And they are not like the books at
your house.

I have to find a new book on ships.

Sam picks out a book to read.
The name of the book is
Animals to Make You Laugh.

Look at the animals in this book.
I see a green lion.
And what is this animal behind the lion?
You can't see animals like this in a zoo.

All I want is a new book on ships.

Now Sam sees a box on top of a chair.
A giant red book is on top of the box.
Sam picks it out to read.
The name of this book is
<u>Lights, Lights, Lights.</u>
The book makes Sam laugh.

 Come and read this book, Kate.

 Are ships in your book?

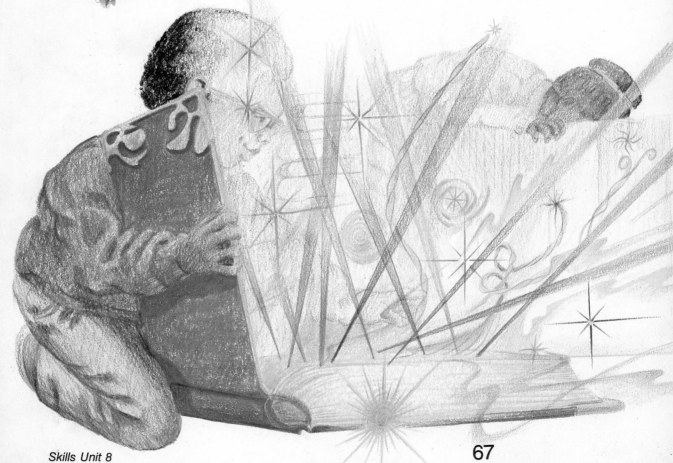

Ships are not in this book.
But look at what it has.
It has lights all over it.
And the lights jump out of the book.
They are jumping over me and behind me.
You have to come and read it.

I can't come to read your book now.
I have to find a new book on ships.

Kate finds a new book on ships.
The name of this book is
Ships to Ride.

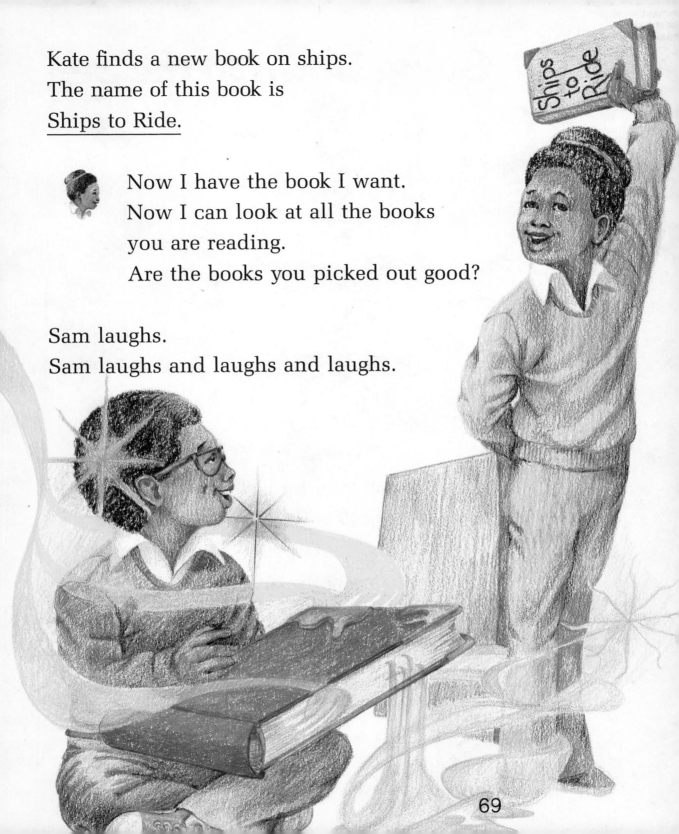

Now I have the book I want.
Now I can look at all the books
you are reading.
Are the books you picked out good?

Sam laughs.
Sam laughs and laughs and laughs.

Going Down to the Sea

Grandpa took Pam for a ride.

Grandpa took Pam down to the sea.

 We are going to see the <u>Lion</u>.

 A lion? Are we going to see a lion?

 <u>Lion</u> is the name of a ship.

We are going to see a ship.

 <u>Lion</u>? What a name for a ship!

 It is a good name for this ship.
The ship is yellow like a lion.
And it has a lion on it.
I sailed on the <u>Lion</u>.
I helped pick out the name.
Look! You can see the <u>Lion</u> now.
It is the ship with lights all over it.

Pam took a good look.

I can see it.

I can see the lights.

And I see sails.

The Lion is a sailing ship!

Can we go on it?

It looks like a good ship.

I want to see all of it.

I want to go to the top.

72

Grandpa took Pam on the <u>Lion</u>.

Grandpa took Pam to the top of the ship.

 You have to hold on, Pam.

Hold on to me.

Now you can look out over the sea.

 I like the sea, Grandpa.
What is it like to sail the sea?

 Sailing is good.
You can go all over.
You can sail to new lands.
You can see all you want to see.

I want to sail with you, Grandpa.

 We can't sail this time, Pam.
The <u>Lion</u> can't go to sea now.
But we are going to find a good time for
sailing.
And you and I can sail all over the sea.

75

Lions to Ride

I want to ride on a lion.
I want a giant yellow lion.
I want to ride all over on it.

I'm a kid.

You make me laugh, Carmen.
You can't ride a lion.
A lion is not a good animal to ride.

But I want to ride on a lion.
I want to find a lion to ride.

76

The zoo has lions.
Look at all the lions the zoo has.
I like all the lions I see.
But they are not good to ride.
The lion I want to ride is not
at the zoo.

I like to ride lions.
I can find you a lion to ride.
Come with me.
Come see the lions I ride.
You are going to like the lions I ride.

78

I see your lions!

I see a red and green lion.

Look behind the red and green lion.

Put me on the giant yellow lion.

Put me on the lion and make it go.

Now I can ride a lion.

I can ride all the lions I want.

MASTERY WORD LISTS

The following high-frequency words (words that appear on recognized word-frequency lists) have been read a minimum of twelve times by the end of this book. Pupils should be able to recognize both the root word and the root word with these endings: s, ed, ing.

The page number printed after each word in the first list shows the word's first appearance in this book. The second list is a cumulative list of previously mastered words.

shop	14	help	19	my	34
come	14	new	20	name	43
me	14	yard	20	behind	50
good	15	jump	30	light	50
giant	16	over	30	laugh	58
zoo	19	out	33	see	64
animal	19	your	33	book	64
we	19	but	34		

a	go	play
all	going	red
and	green	run
are	has	table
at	have	the
blue	house	they
box	I	this
boy	in	to
can	is	under
can't	it	want
cold	like	what
down	look	with
find	make	yellow
for	not	you
get	now	
girl	on	

LEVEL 2B

Scott, Foresman and Company

Scott, Foresman Reading

On Our Own

THIS BOOK IS THE PROPERTY OF:

STATE _____

PROVINCE _____

COUNTY _____

PARISH _____

SCHOOL DISTRICT _____

OTHER _____

Book No. _____

Enter information
in spaces
to the left as
instructed.

ISSUED TO	Year Used	CONDITION	
		ISSUED	RETURNED
Chad			
Andrew			
Jill			
Freida			
Chaz			
Michelle			
April-Greene			

PUPILS to whom this textbook is issued must not write on any page
or mark any part of it in any way, consumable textbooks excepted.

1. Teachers should see that the pupil's name is clearly written in ink in the spaces above in every book issued.
2. The following terms should be used in recording the condition of the book: New; Good; Fair; Poor; Bad.